WALLAS PENA

VIBRATO MASTERY

VIOLA

BOOK I

FIRST EDITION

CONTENTS

PREFACE

I have never believed that musicality is something that is impossible to learn or explain! Unfortunately, there is an understanding that musicality belongs to a select few, and everybody else should accept it. I devoted countless hours of my life to studying the greatest artists of all time, so I could help other people find their voices. After years of research, I concluded that great musicality shares the same foundation. This book is the first iteration of my findings documented.

Musicality is often subjective; artists talk about feelings, colors, and images, but rarely about how to consistently create emotions regardless of inspiration. The only way to rationally organize musicality is through mathematics. Once a process is understood, it becomes reproducible; this eliminates the subjective nature of musicality. At first, it sounds cold, but mathematics will free your musicianship. For this book, I decided to hide the complicated mathematics behind meticulously crafted exercises.

Vibrato is one of the most fundamental aspects of music, which is why I chose it as the first subject of my book series on musicality. This book will help you understand the intricacies of vibrato and its mechanics.

This book was primarily written for those who can vibrate already, although it is invaluable to have this knowledge early on in your career.

INTRODUCTION

Many people believe that vibrato is like a fingerprint, but once you understand its inner workings, you will be able to analyze and reproduce anybody's vibrato. It is not easy for artists to accept that art can be quantified or explained, but we should celebrate that mathematics can help us understand such a complex subject.

My research confirmed that, contrary to popular belief, vibrato is below and above the note and not just below. Our brain registers the middle pitch and not the highest, as many people believe. If you only vibrate below the target note, you will sound constricted and slightly flat. The optimal vibrato width should be a semitone, which means quarter tones below and above the target note. The width will vary based on the music's character; most of the time, it will be narrower than a semitone, and rarely will it be wider. If you want to vibrate below the note only, this book will work just as well, but I urge you to try it and see for yourself how great below and above vibrato sounds. That is what great singers and instrumentalists did in the past and what great artists continue to do today. The choice is yours.

I organized vibrato speeds in the easiest way I could find; I called them vibrato 4, vibrato 5, and vibrato 6; each represents a specific number of cycles relative to the music's tempo. A cycle consists of two individual oscillations, the higher and the lower. Each vibrato speed has its own innate characteristics. Choose which vibrato sounds better at any particular moment; this is the basis of expressive vibrato.

The vibrato's speed should be compatible with the music's tempo; it has to make sense rhythmically, and it has to be a perfect subdivision. No fixed vibrato speed is going to work for everything; one should always keep that in mind. The finger rolling should be even going back and forth between the higher and lower pitches; both are equally important, although individual cycle counting happens at the higher pitch. Do not get stuck on either pitch; evenness is the key.

Vibrato will mostly range between 45 and 60 BPM, even when playing fast music. For example, if you are playing a piece of music at 120 BPM, the vibrato will actually be performed at 60 BPM, as 120 BPM would be way too fast. By the same logic, if you are playing at 130 BPM, the vibrato will be at 65 BPM.

VIBRATO SPEEDS

Vibrato 5

This is the single most important vibrato speed; if you were to choose only one for the rest of your life, this is it. Now you know one of the secrets behind the greatest artists. This speed works for almost anything, whether it's the climax or the most intimate part of the music, as long as you pay attention to its width; as a general rule, the louder the music, the wider it is; the softer the music, the narrower it is. It could be a bit of a challenge to get used to the feeling of quintuplets, but I promise you the results will be amazing.

Vibrato 6

This speed is ideal for intense moments. It takes work to control it, but the results are incredible; this is the vibrato you hear from great singers or instrumentalists at the climax of their performances. This is the vibrato that will impress audiences. Do not be afraid to use it.

Vibrato 4

This vibrato sits on the slow side. It works well for introspective moments and continuous vibrato when playing sixteenth notes. It is not commonly used for intense moments, as it lacks excitement. I could hear some great singers using this vibrato at intense moments where loudness was the most important factor, as the slower speed makes it easier to use a larger width.

MECHANICS EXERCISES

These exercises introduce the inner mechanics of vibrato. Expressive vibrato is measured, and that is what these exercises aim to achieve. They are a slowed-down version of the actual vibrato. Fingers should always roll from one oscillation to the other. Do not slide; only change fingers every other two bars, as written in the exercises. Practice slowly with the utmost attention. For those not familiar with quarter tone notation, the flats and sharps used in the first two mechanics exercises are quarter tones and not semitones.

I - Get used to the feeling of going below and above the note; keep in mind that the quarter tone above is narrower than the bellow; if you go too high, it will sound sharp. Do not connect the bars; practice each bar until you feel comfortable playing each finger.

II - This represents perfect vibrato oscillations. The finger lands on the target note; then it goes below and above, keeps going back and forth between below and above until there is a note change that will land on the target pitch, and so on and so forth. The bowing represents the two oscillations per note, which is the heart of my vibrato method.

III - Same goal as the first exercise, but this time it concentrates on the feeling of a semitone below the note.

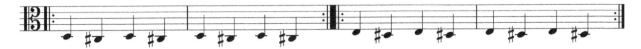

IV - The same goal as the second, but it concentrates on the vibrato below the note.

HOW TO USE THIS BOOK

Each note in the main section of this book represents one cycle, which means that every bowing also contains one cycle. The exercises in this book aim to help you develop control of specific vibrato speeds and all their individual cycles at every metronome marking. As said before, please pay attention to the use of quarter tone notation in the example. Exercises are written in D major, first position, but must be practiced in all keys and positions you see fit.

One should always practice with a metronome and gradually increase the tempo; I recommend practicing a different tempo every other day, going from 45 to 90 BPM.

The example below shows one of the exercises and a representation of its inner mechanics.

Should sound like

The example below shows a representation of the same exercise, but this time it goes below the note only.

Should sound like

When speed, width, and bow change are perfectly synchronized, you will have achieved great vibrato. It is imperative that you play with width; you will be amazed at the number of possible colors. Learn the rules so you can break them. My second book on vibrato will go in-depth on breaking the rules and many other aspects of the artistic use of vibrato. Be creative!

VIBRATO EXERCISES

1 - The first variation aims to get you comfortable with the speed and width of the target vibrato. Repeat until you feel comfortable with every finger. Do not connect the bars. Do not move on until you can vibrate correctly.

2 - The second variation starts to connect the notes, setting you up not only for vibrato control but also for continuous vibrato. The change for the following note starts at the end of the previous, which is how you create a never-ending continuous vibrato.

3 - The third exercise is equal to the second, but the notes change faster.

4 - The fourth variation checks if your vibrato is respecting the target speed and width. The long notes should keep the same speed and width as the short ones. Practice with the utmost attention. Do not proceed to the next bar until you feel comfortable.

5 - The fifth variation aims to get you comfortable playing regular half notes at the speed and width you are practicing. Remember that the change to the following note happens at the end of the previous note. Only change the bow's direction after the next finger is on the string. Every change should happen before the downbeat.

6 - The sixth variation is equal to the fifth, but faster.

VIBRATO MECHANICS

Vibrato Mechanics I

♩ = 45-90

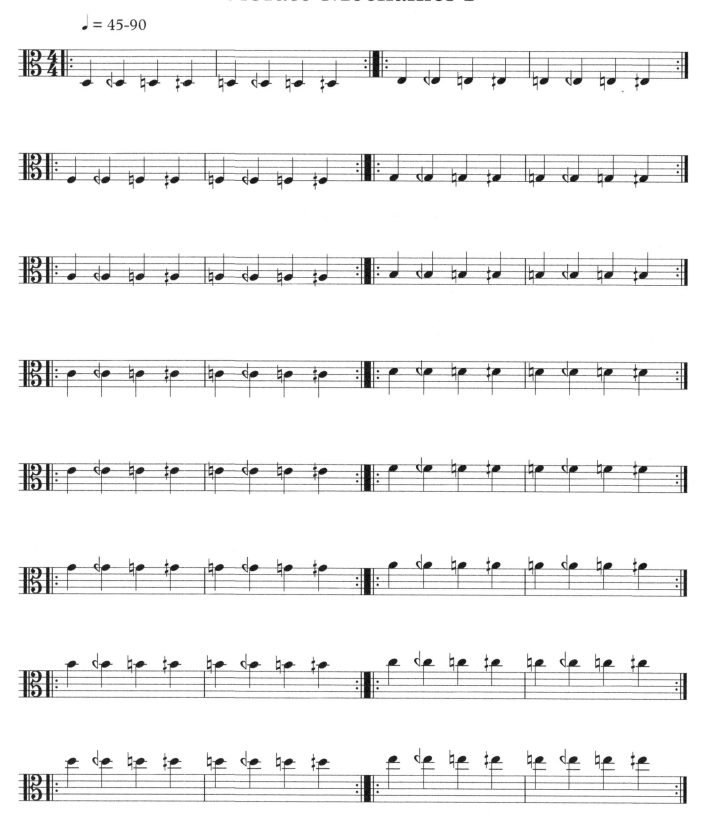

Vibrato Mechanics II

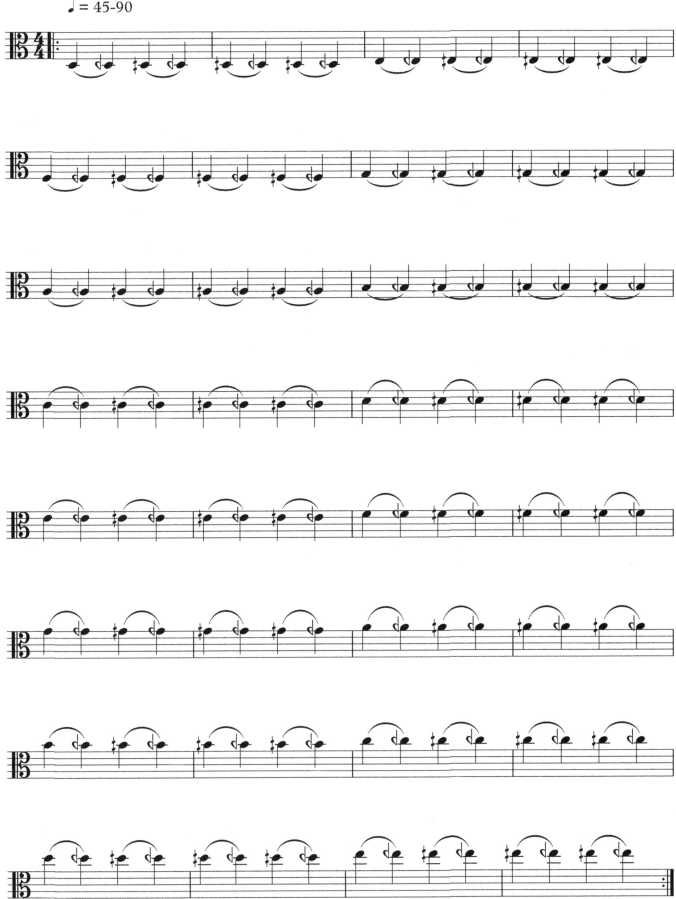

4

Vibrato Mechanics III

♩ = 45-90

Vibrato Mechanics IV

VIBRATO 5

I

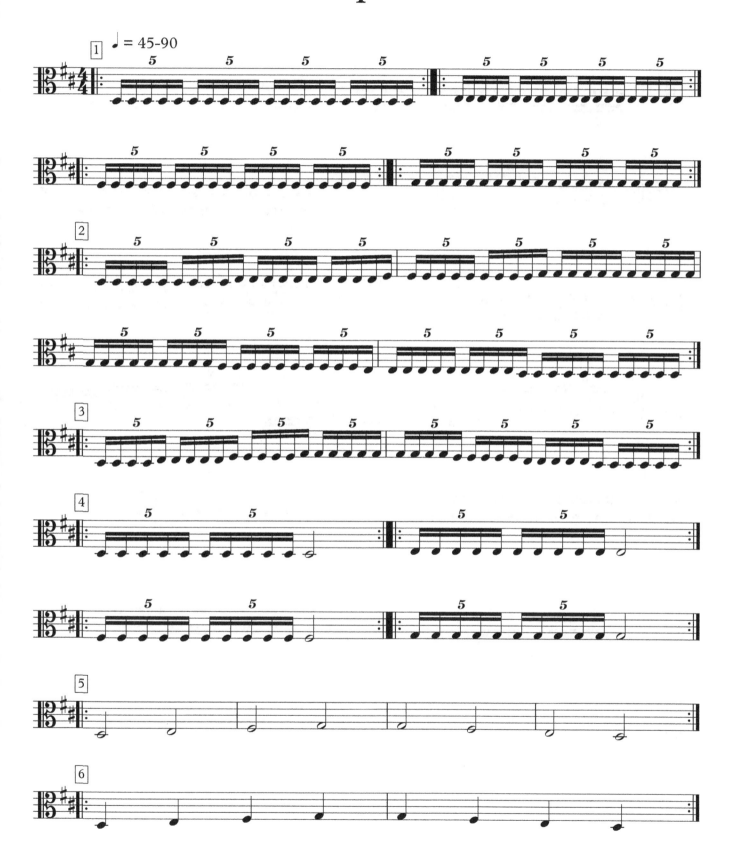

II

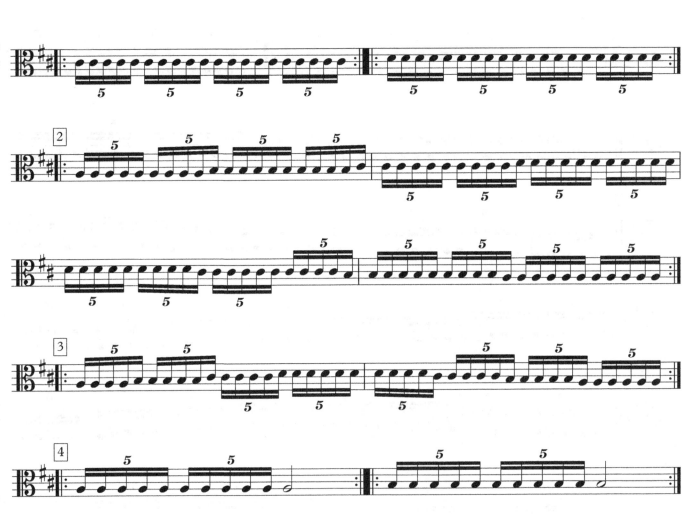

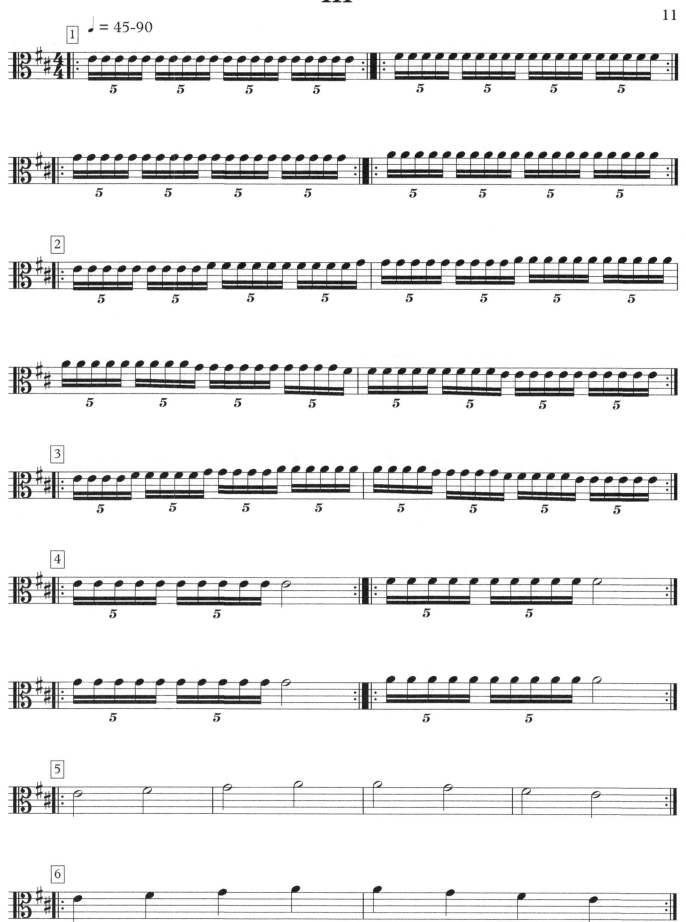

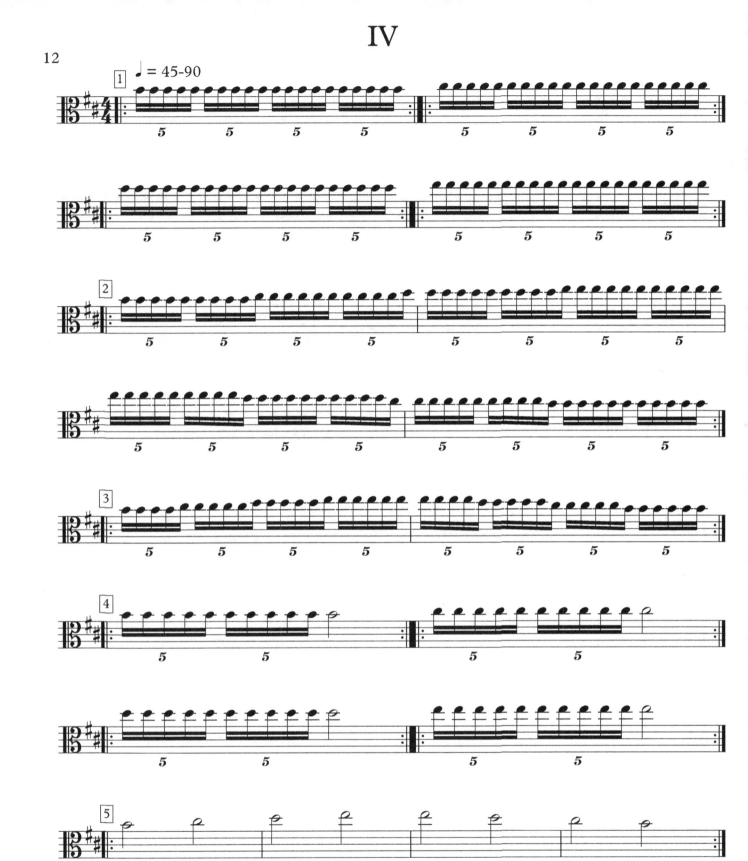

V

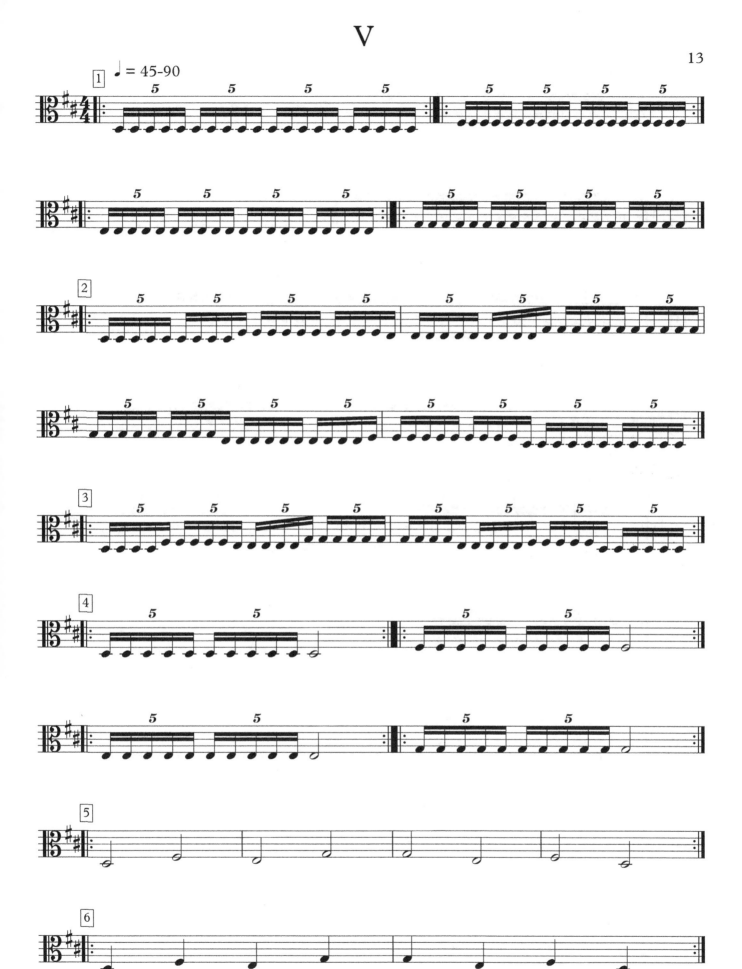

VII

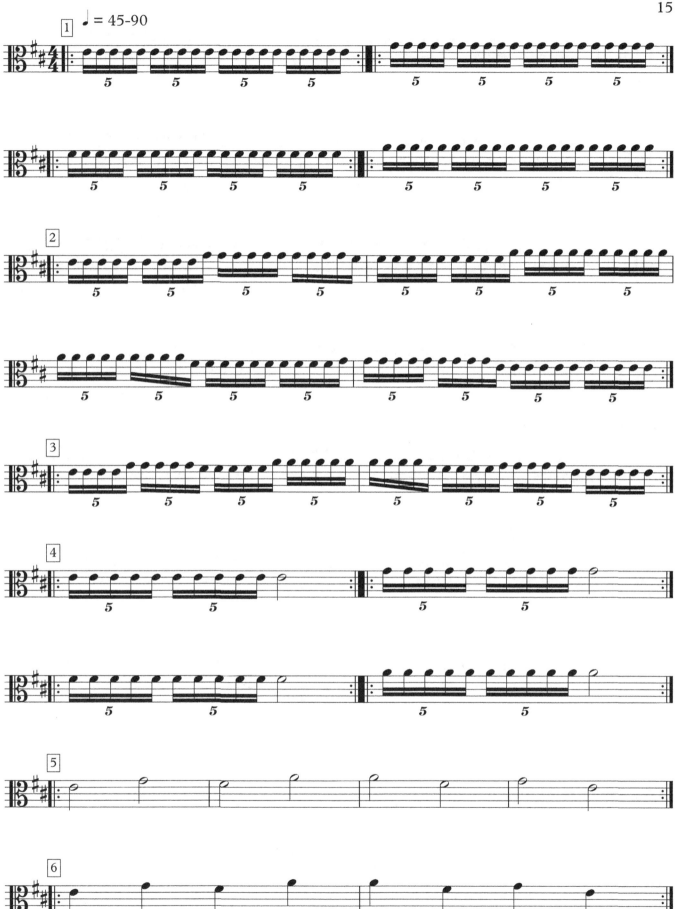

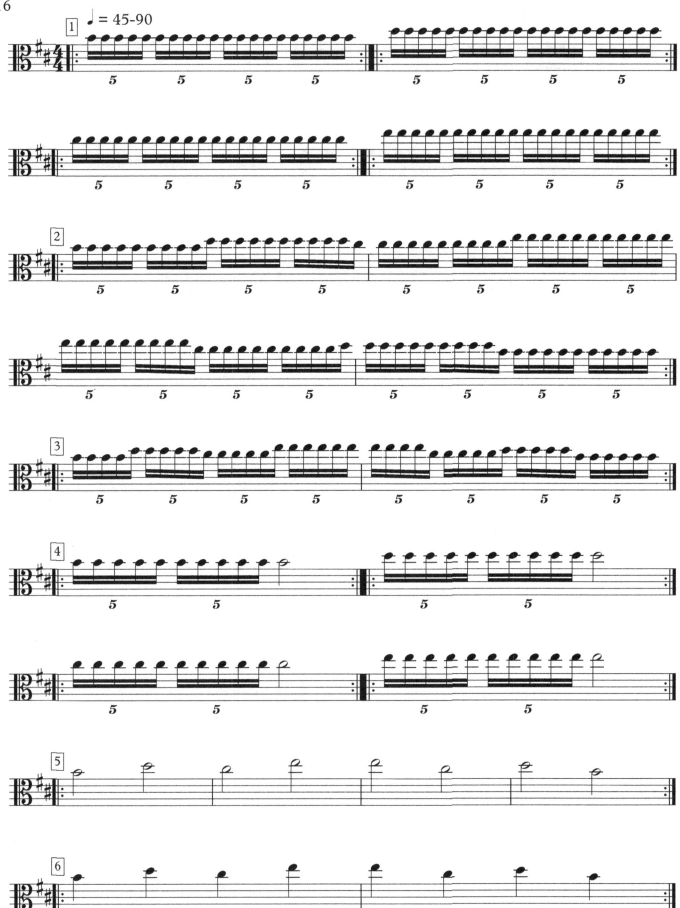

IX

X

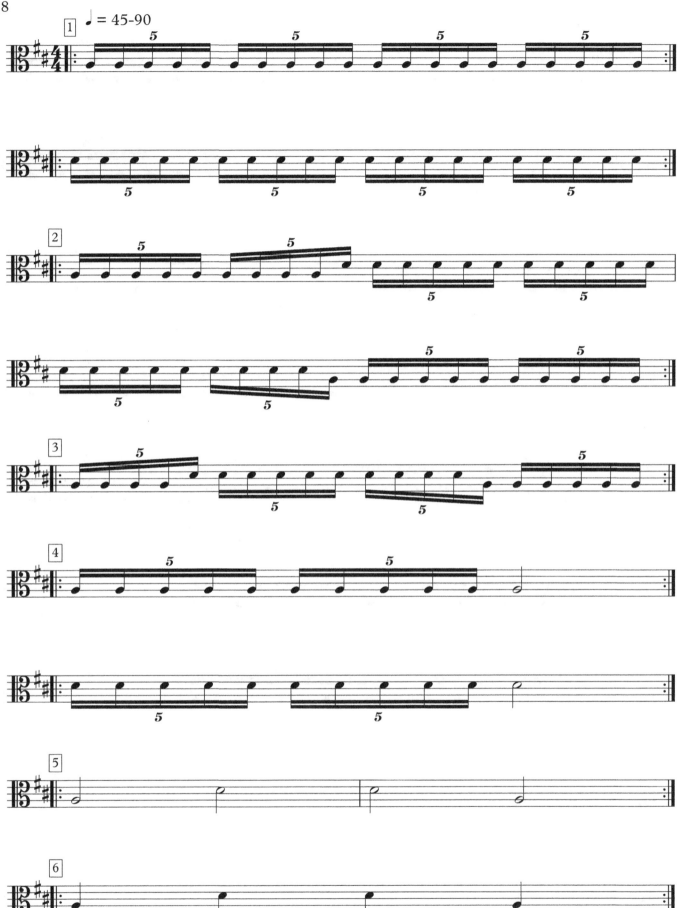

XI

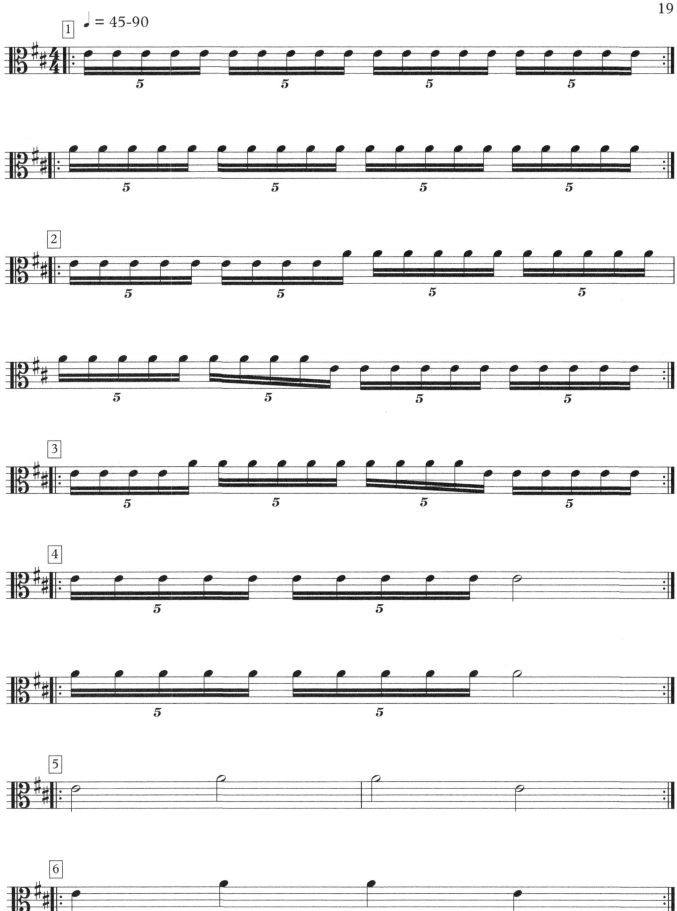

XII

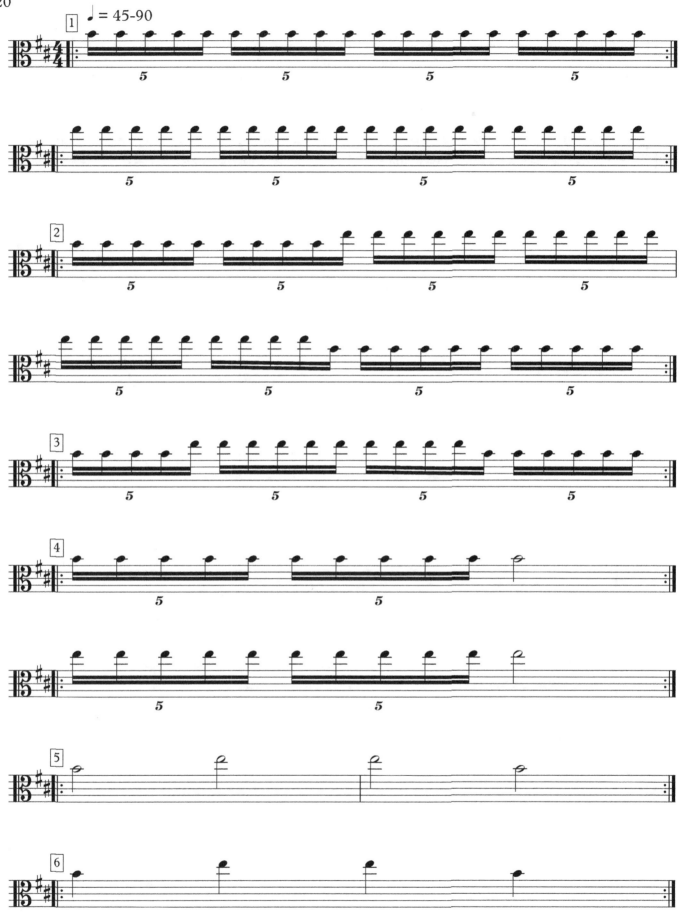

XIII

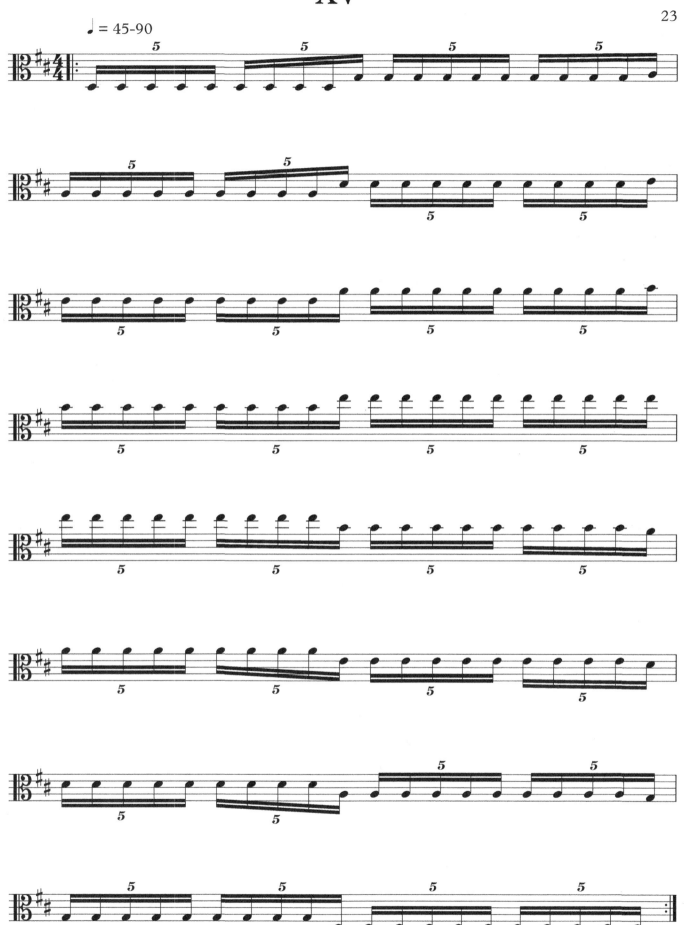

VIBRATO 6

I

II

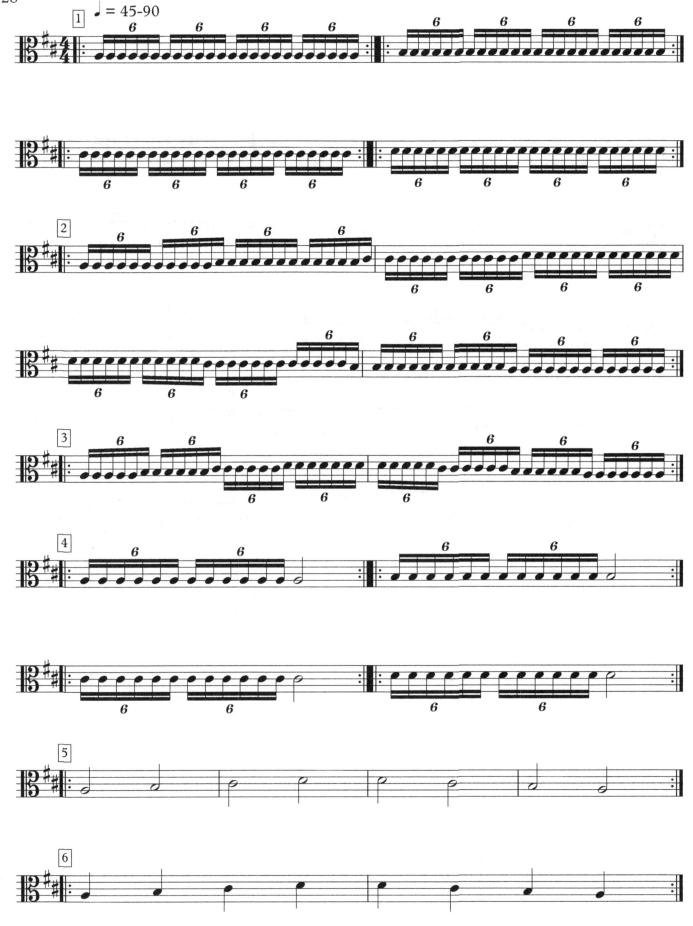

III

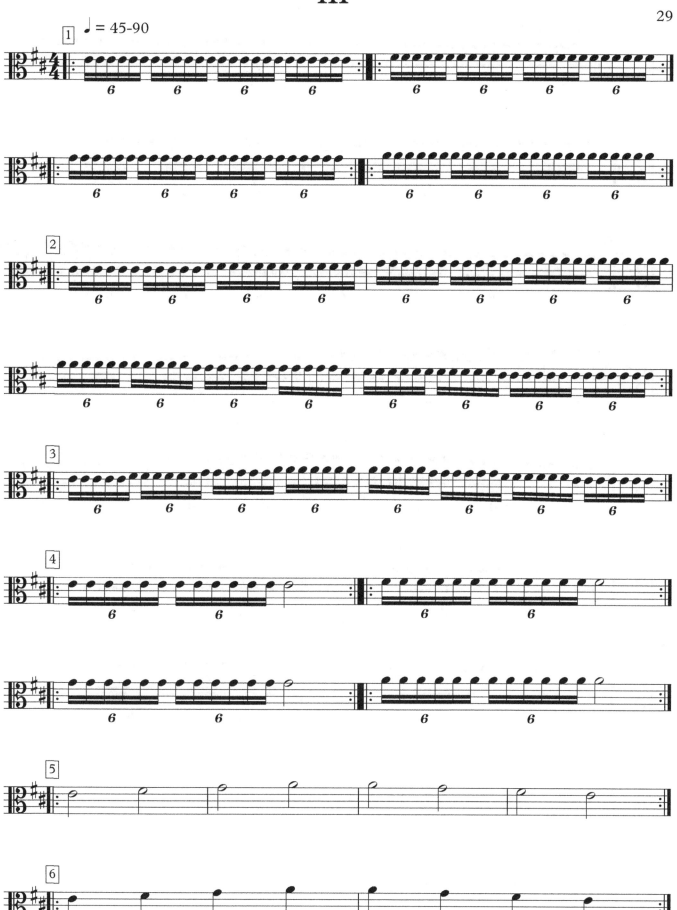

IV

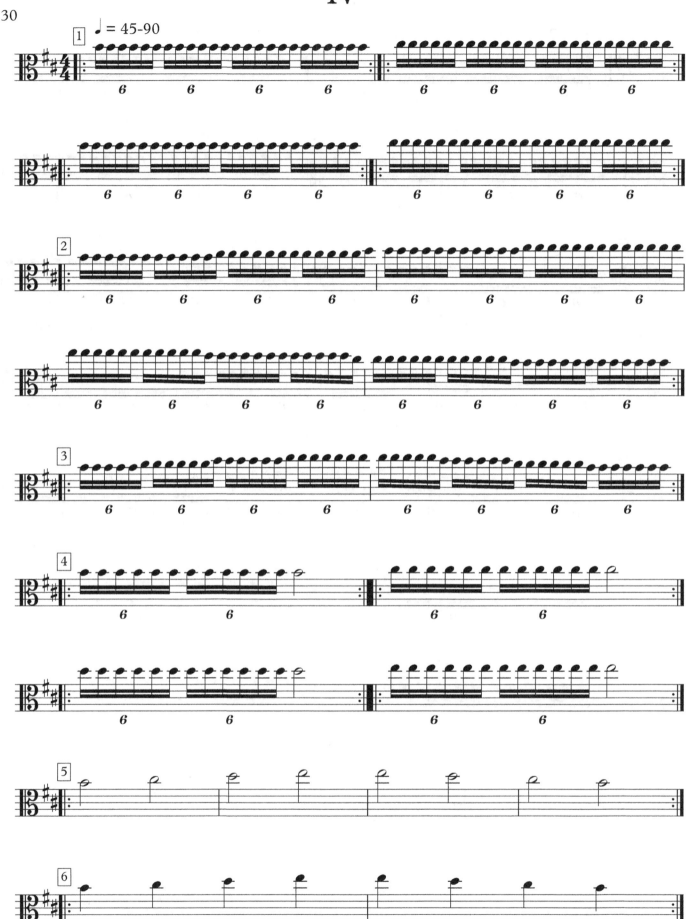

VI

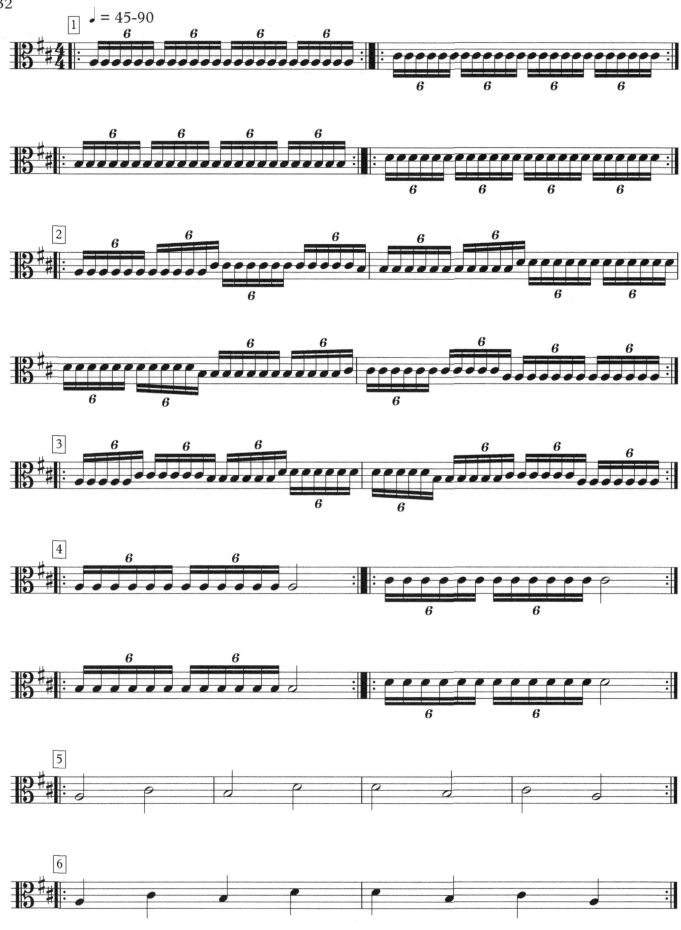

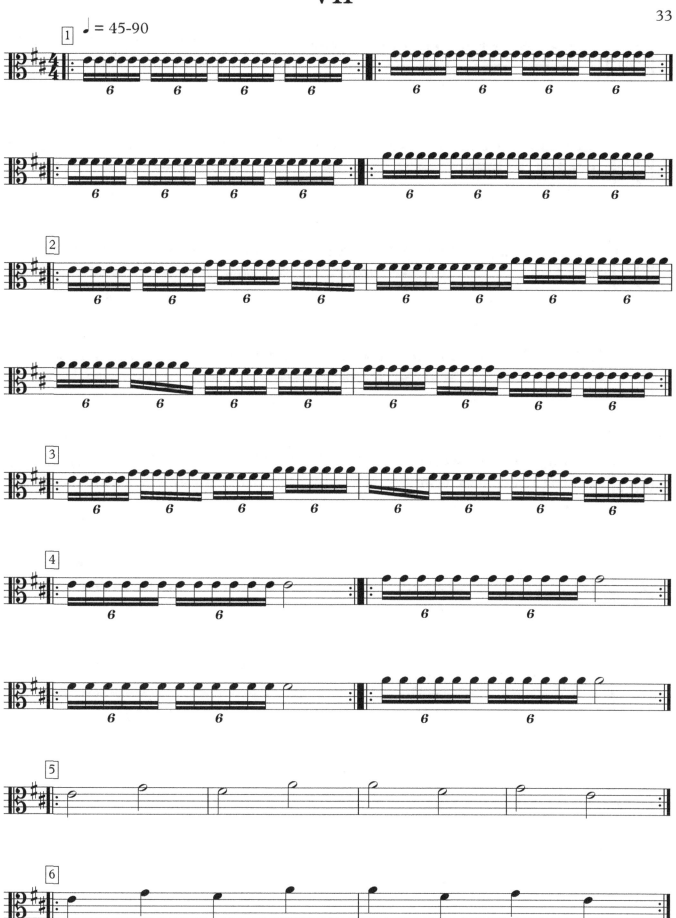

VIII

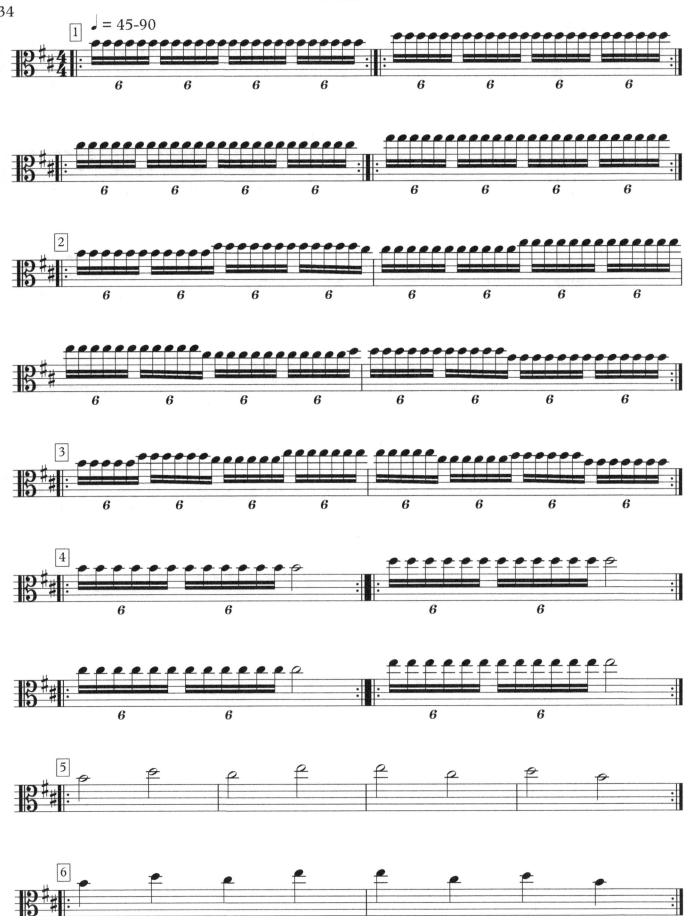

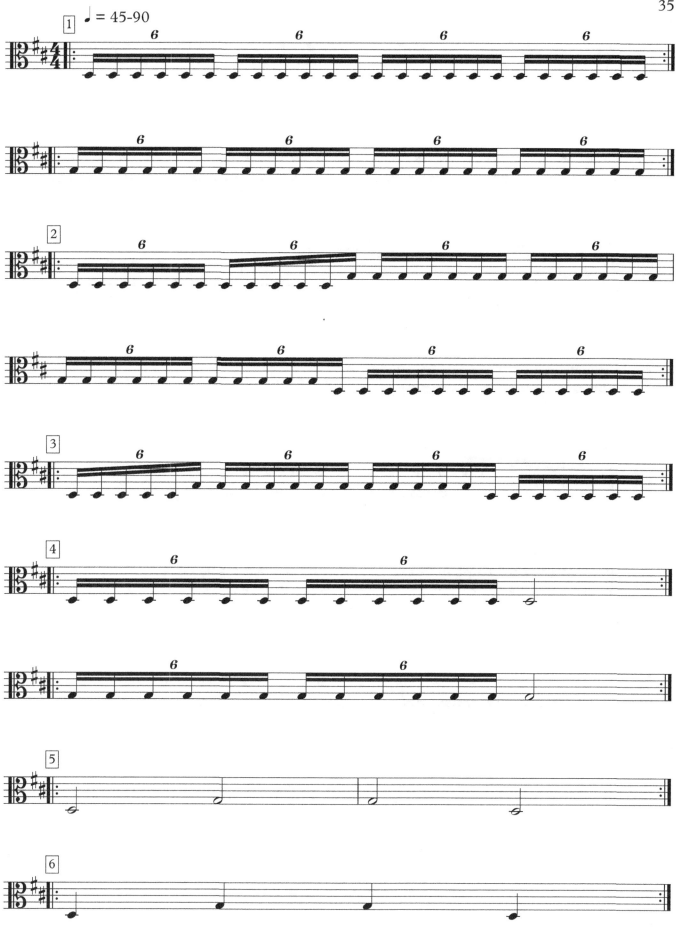

X

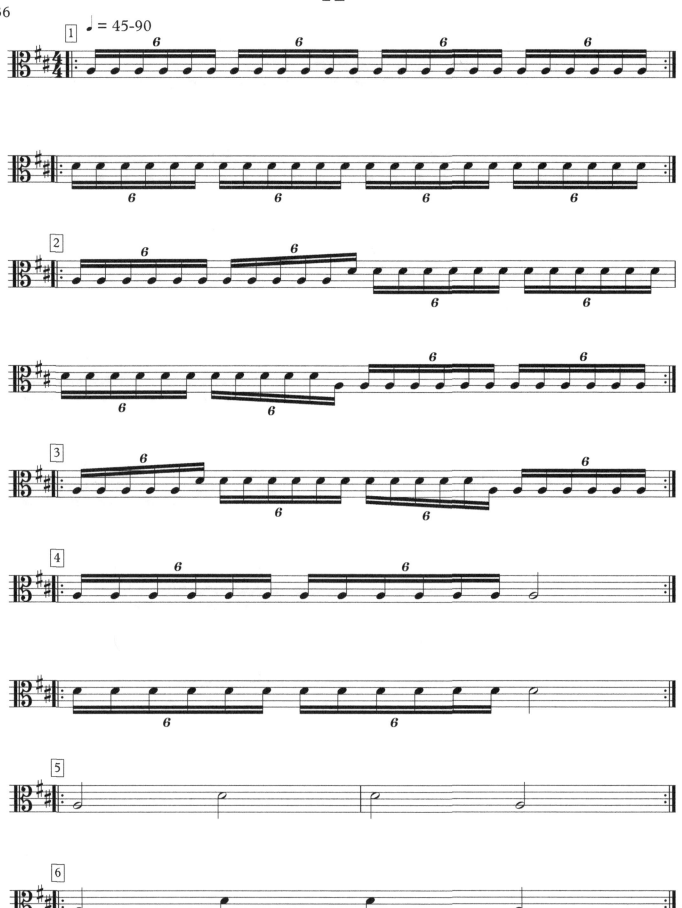

XI

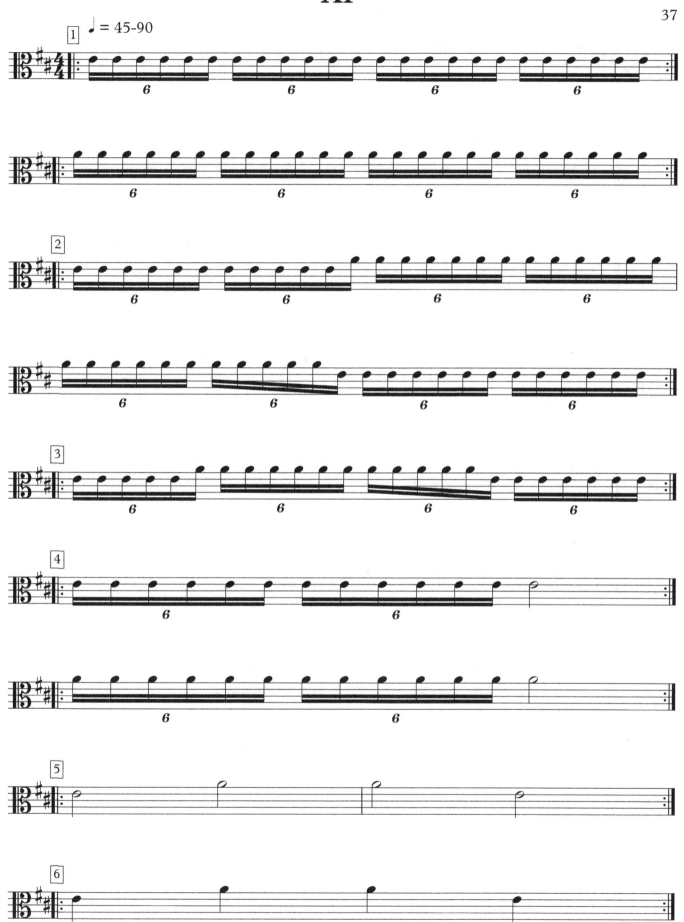

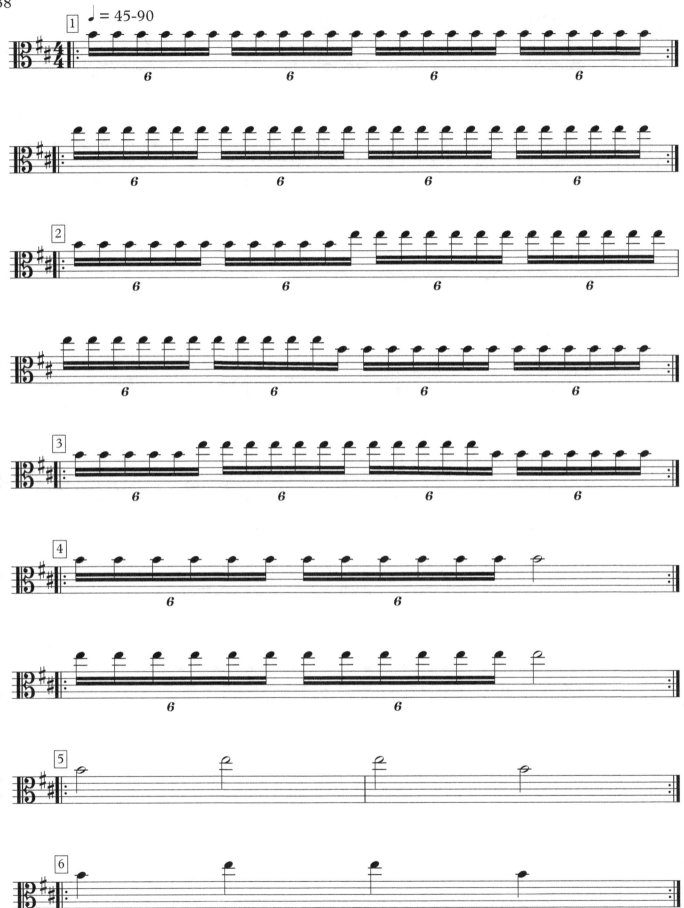

XIII

40

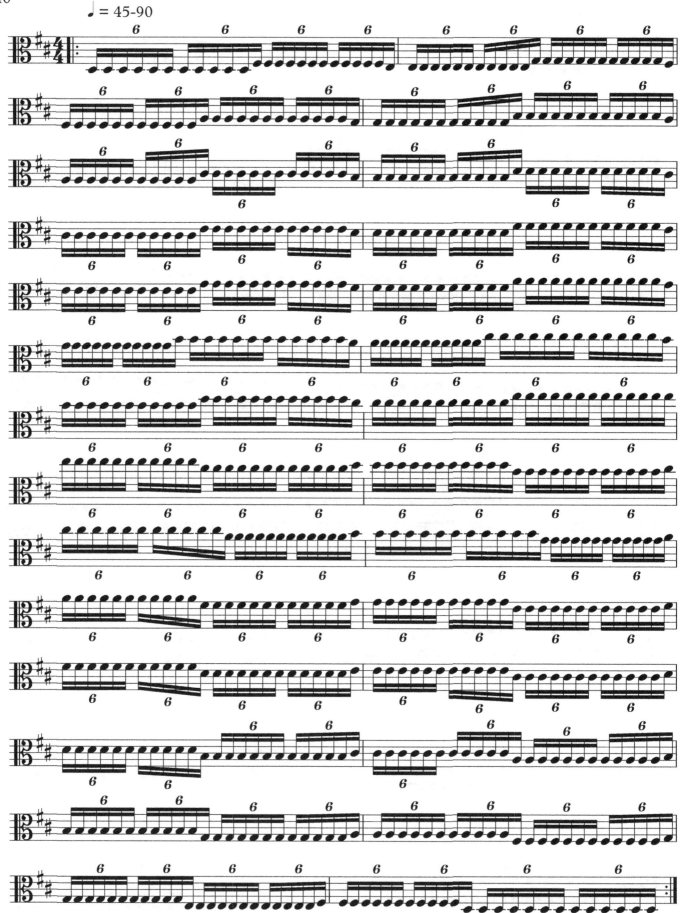

XV

VIBRATO 4

I

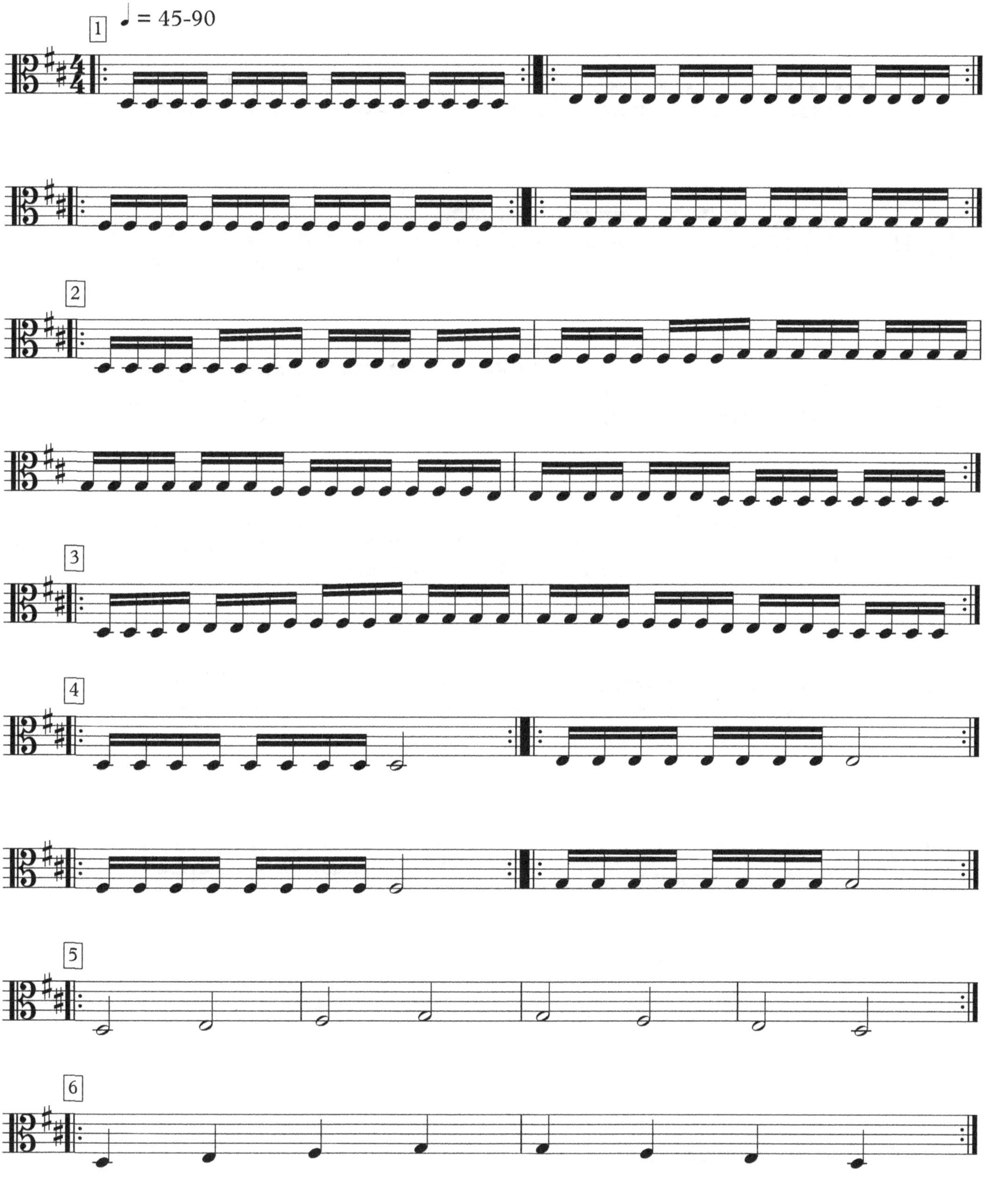

II

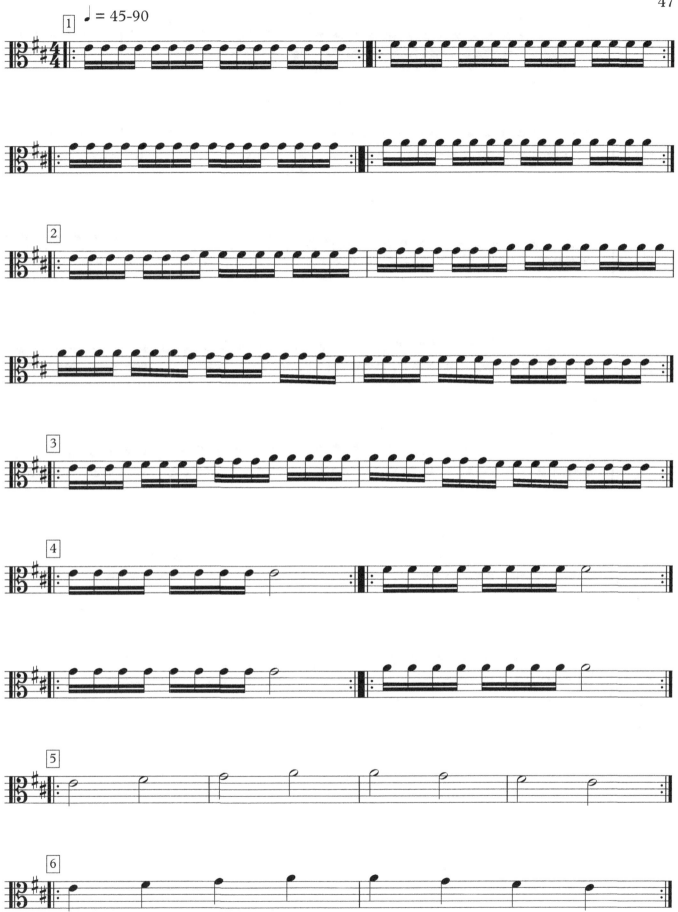

IV

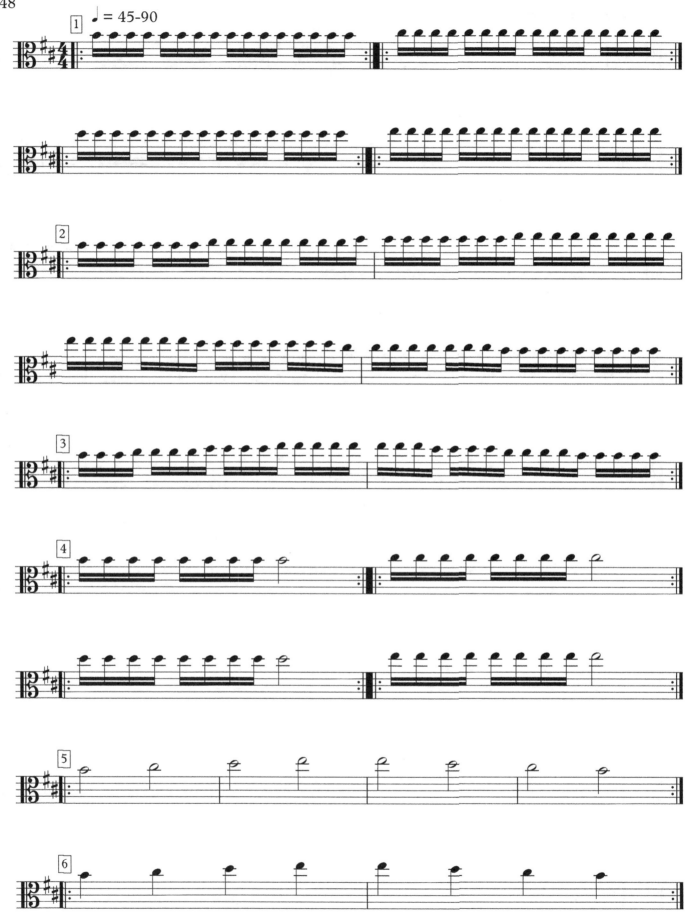

VI

VIII

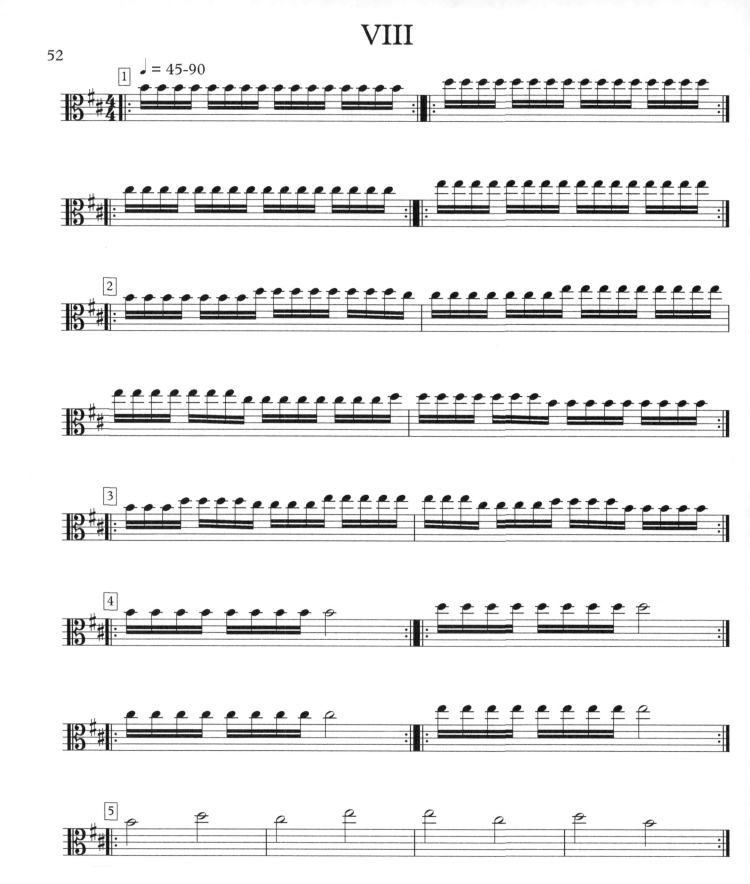

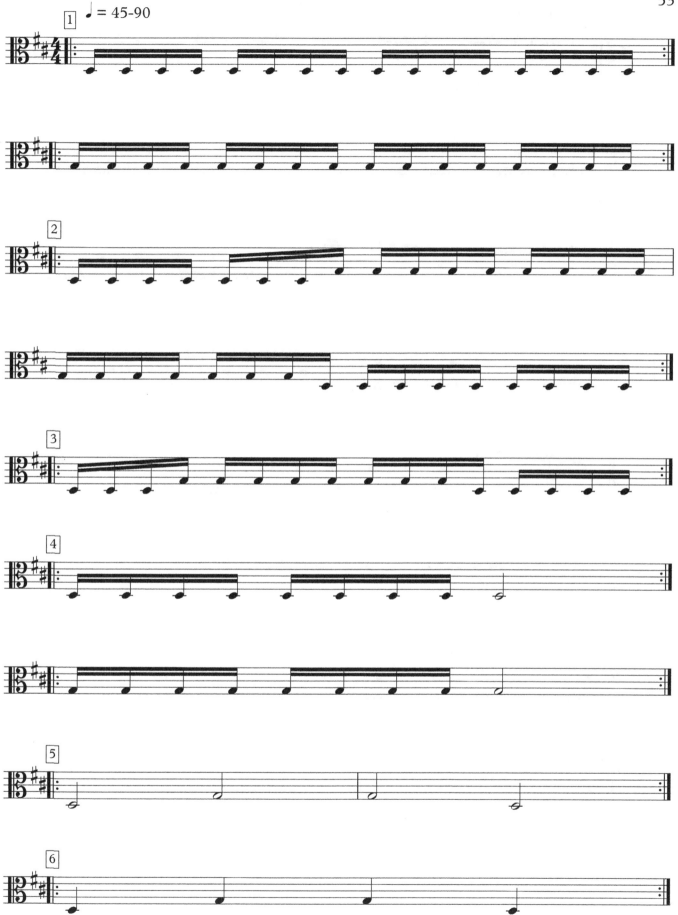

X

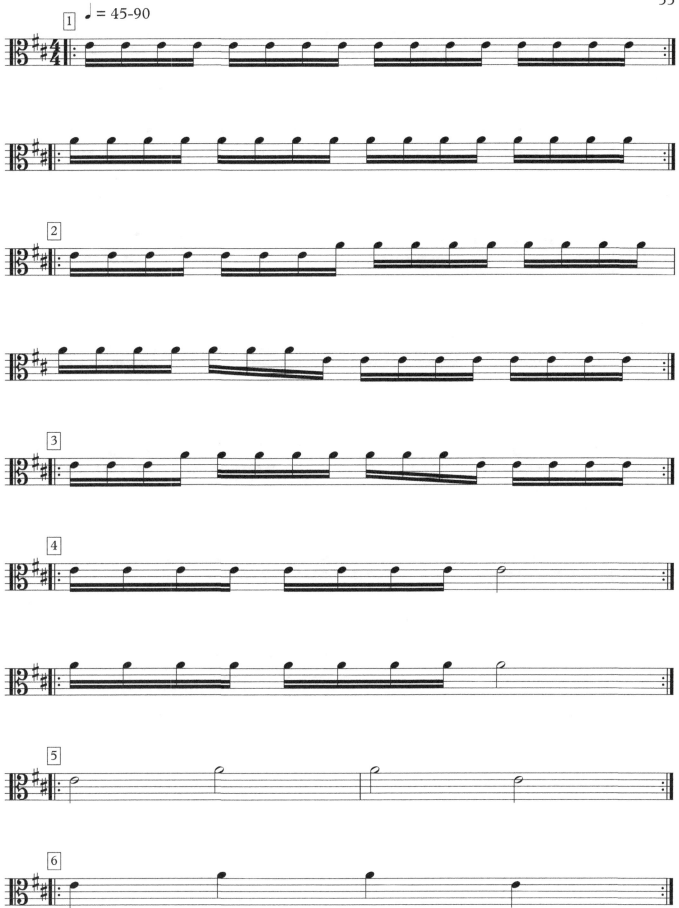

XII

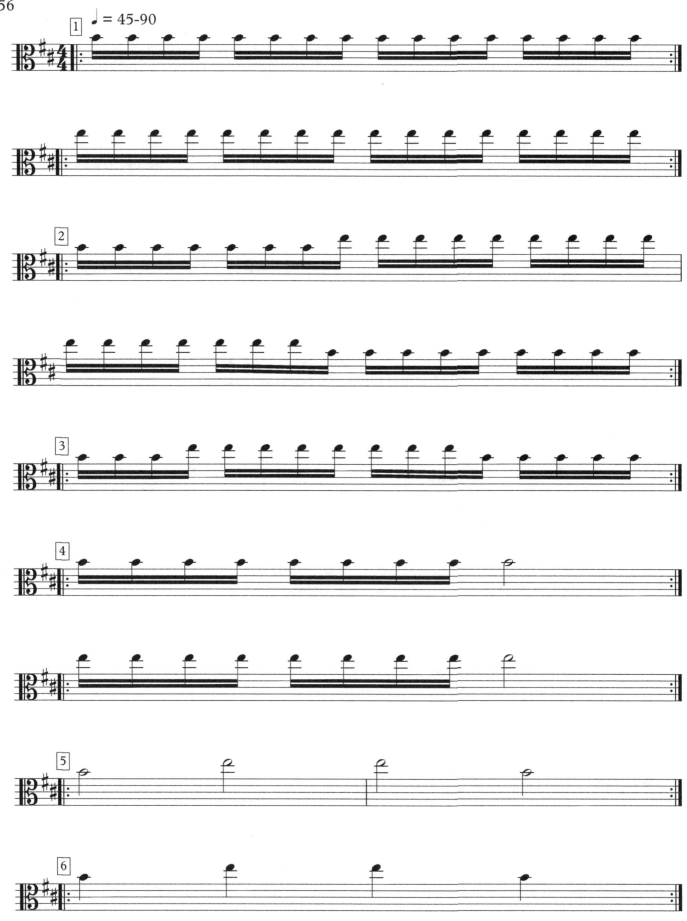

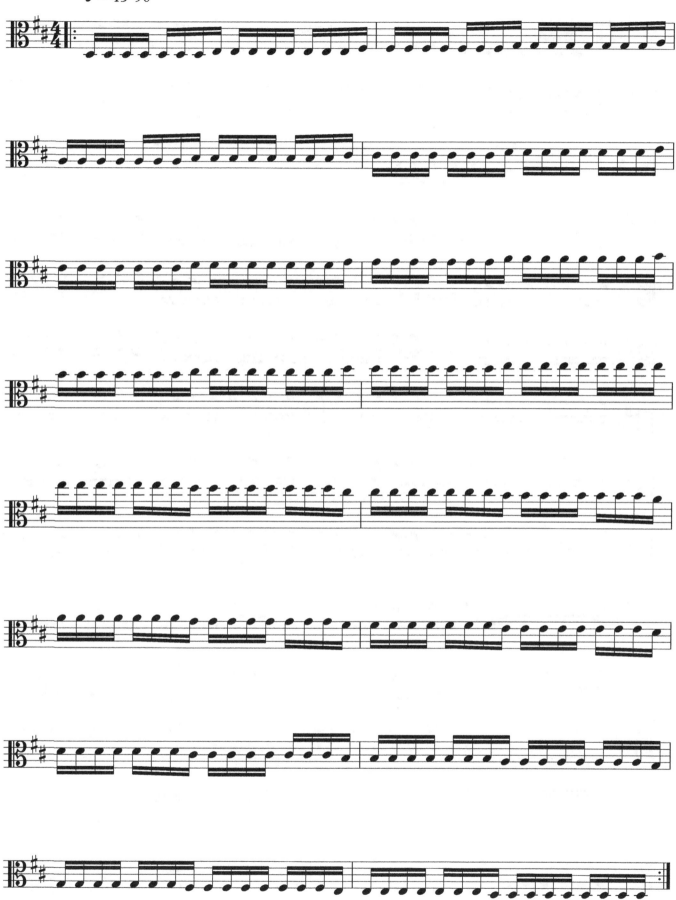

58

♩ = 45-90

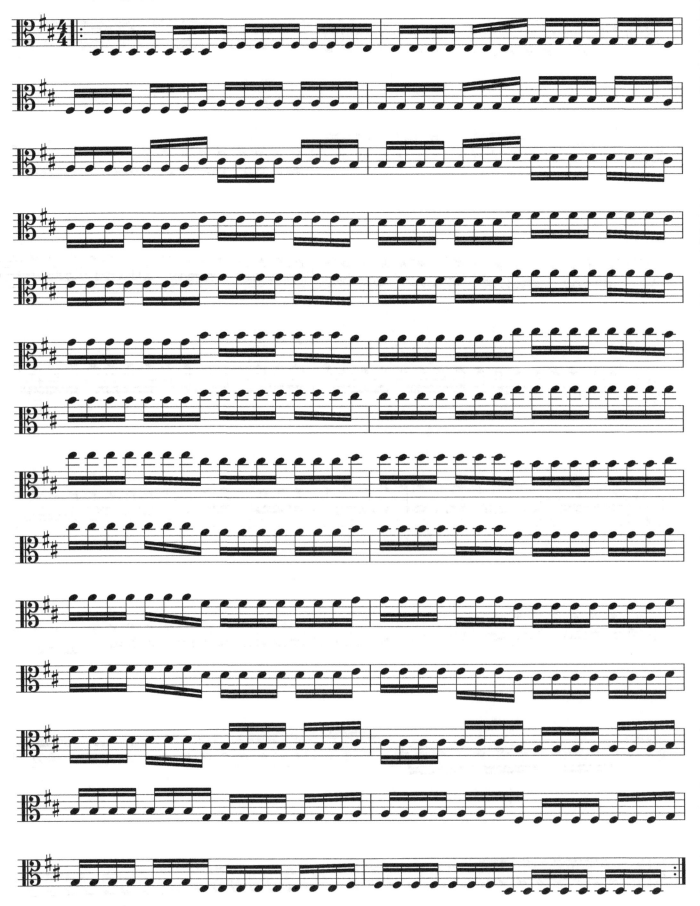

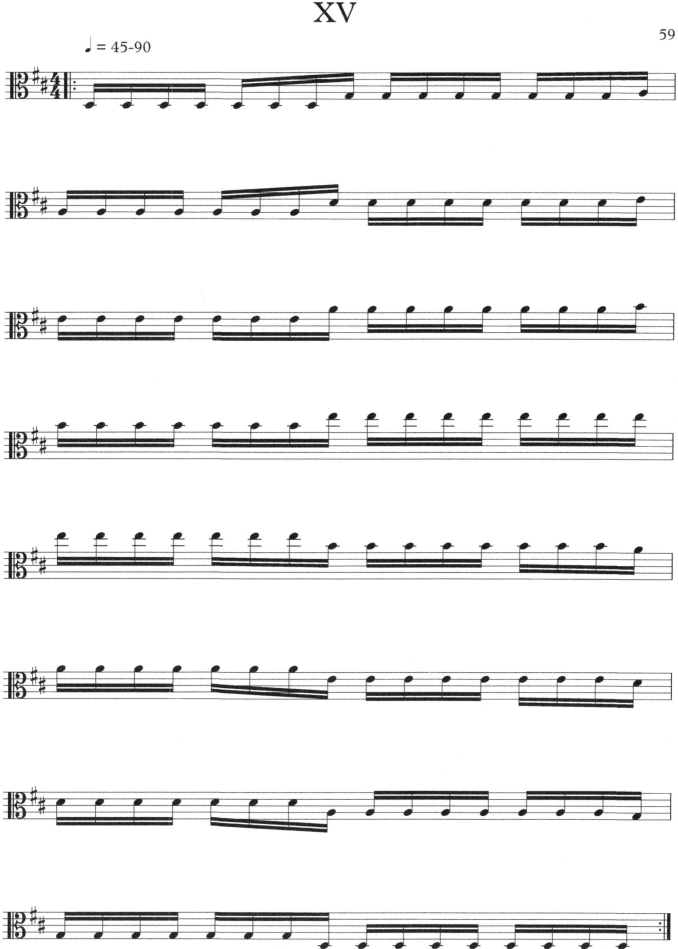

ABOUT THE AUTHOR

Wallas Pena is an accomplished violist and musicality researcher.
For the Vibrato Mastery Online Course, visit:
www.wallaspena.com

Made in the USA
Monee, IL
28 April 2022